Rhythm Kids

Rhymes and Fun Time Exercises For Babies

By Pauline Carpenter
and
Anita Epple

Illustrations by
Alison Carpenter-Hughes

Ditto International Ltd

Published and distributed in Great Britain by
Ditto International Ltd, Unit 2, Elms Farm Industrial Park, Bramshall,
Staffordshire ST14 5BE
www.touchneeds.com

Printed in Great Britain by Parker & Collinson Ltd
ISBN 978-0-9545188-1-3

Acknowledgments

*To our children, who have inspired us to sing rhymes
and play with them over the years*

*Also, thanks to Sam, Lowell, John and Josh
Zoe, Greg and Sophia*

Contents

The Fun-Time Exercises:

1. Warm Up And Floor Exercises

For these rhymes you will need to sit on the floor, with your baby on a mat in front of you

2. Standing Exercises

For these rhymes you will need to be standing up, holding your baby securely in your arms

3. Floor Exercises

For these rhymes you will need to be on the floor, holding your baby

4. Cooling Down Exercises

For these rhymes you will need to sit on the floor, with your baby on a mat in front of you, except for Sleep Baby Sleep, when you need to hold them in your arms

Foreword

The first language of life is one of movement. The experience of movement is shared by every living thing, from the rotation of the earth to hearing the sighing of the trees in the wind and the birds sing. Movement is present at the creation of human life when cellular movement, union and division first take place and from his tiny, private ocean inside the womb, the developing baby feels every movement his mother makes. Movement is involved in sensory perception, in the expression of life (quickening), in emotion (meaning "to move") and all forms of communication.

Babies and young children learn with their bodies before they learn with their heads and physical experience and interaction are as vital to early development as nutrition. Within hours of birth babies can mimic simple gestures like sticking their tongue out. Although speech does not start to emerge until the end of the first year of life, the infant (meaning, one without speech) is already an effective communicator using his body and his voice to express his feelings, his needs and his dislikes. The cooing of the young baby has melody, rhythm and intonation. "Conversations" between mother and baby begin with gentle vocalisation and facial expression - mother and baby time their interactions to watch, listen and talk to one another. Rhythm is an expression of movement in time and space. In this sense, movement and music are the first vocabulary of life - the sounds and gestures of pre-language on which more formal speech will be built.

In simpler times, before the invention of electronic recording devices and ever busier lives, lullabies, nursery rhymes and physical play were a natural part of mother-child interaction. These activities help to familiarise the young child with the rhythms, cadences and intonation of speech long before he or she learns to speak - as an accomplished mimic, the baby learns to copy these patterns and combine them with gesture and movement to develop a sound basis for language. Lullabies carry rhythms that are soothing, nursery rhymes help to build a lexicon of similar sounds as well as telling a story and being structured in time patterns that make one want to move in time to the music.

Babies love and respond in different ways to different kinds of movement. Movement is the medium through which the different senses are entrained and learn to work together to support posture, balance and coordination. In our modern world, movement and music for babies are as important as they have ever been; nursery rhymes and games are a part of our oral heritage, which we pass on to our children through play. This book provides parents with ideas and activities using the wisdom of past generations to teach children of the future the first language of life.

Sally Goddard Blythe MSc. FRSA
Director of The Institute for Neuro-Physiological Psychology, Chester
Author of "The Well Balanced Child" and "Reflexes, Learning and Behaviour"

Why Sing Rhymes And Do Fun-Time Exercises With Your Baby?

The experiences in the first two to three years of life are so important for the emotional, cognitive and social development of an individual. During these formative years, parents can offer an enriching home environment for their child to learn in, by including singing and fun-time exercises as part of their daily routine.

Nursery rhymes are entrenched in history and form part of our linguistic customs and traditions. When sung they can enhance synchronicity between parent and baby, as they are a wonderful communication tool allowing for enjoyable interactive, quality time. In addition, research shows that they are also a powerful learning tool, because singing to babies and children and encouraging them to join in, when they are able to, is actually having a beneficial effect on the development of the brain. This is because positive stimuli and experiences reinforce neural pathways and increase connectivity.

The use of rhymes, when frequently repeated, play a vital role in the development of language, as the sounds will be stored in their brain for later recovery, even when the meaning of the words are not understood. A baby's memory is built through repeated experiences.

The beneficial, repetitive element of singing rhymes is further enhanced when accompanied by rhythmical exercises, which can help a child retain their flexibility, gain strength and improve muscle tone; as well as potentially enhancing the development of co-ordination and balance. The art of balancing requires adequate muscle tone and postural control. Sight, hearing, spatial awareness and the vestibular system (located in the inner ear) also play an important role in our ability to balance.

Movement is vital to the development of the vestibular system. So it is important that babies are given the opportunity to move about and experience the world from different perspectives and angles in order for the vestibular system to receive daily stimulation; particularly in today's society where babies are often carried in a forward facing position for the majority of the day.

When working through the fun-time exercises your baby will have the opportunity to experience play-time on the floor, in your arms and balanced on your legs. They will be able to see the world from all dimensions and feel what it is like to be turned around, swayed from side to side and lifted up and down.

The rhymes and exercises allow you to help your baby learn, develop and play whilst having fun!

It is important to plan the routine to fit in with your baby's wants and desires. If your baby is happy they may wish to do all the exercises, or only some. They may show preference for a favourite rhyme or exercise that they want you to do several times with them. There may be some exercises that they prefer not to do. When using the book and CD be guided by your baby.

As your child passes from infant to toddler and beyond they will begin to take an interest in looking at books. Your child will then be able to enjoy the colourful pictures that accompany the rhymes, as well as being able to sing along with you.

Preparing The Exercise Space

As well as your Rhythm Kids Book, you will need:
1. CD player
2. A thin (preferably see-through) square scarf
3. Two little finger puppets (optional)
4. Change mat
5. Comfortable clothing for you and your baby

Try to make sure the environment is calm. The room should be warm and with no overhead lights shining directly into your baby's eyes.

You can include older siblings in this constructive play time, by either getting them to do some of the floor exercises, or following what you do with their doll or teddy.

When Not To Do The Exercises

Always find the right time in the day to exercise with your baby, it is important to never practise on a distressed baby. If your baby becomes upset during the routine, it is OK to stop for a cuddle for a little while; or if they have had enough, it is OK to stop until another time.

Never rush. It is important that the time is right for you as well.

Never force an exercise. If your baby does not like an action or rhyme, it is OK to leave it out of their specific routine.

Never practise the exercises with your baby if they are unwell, it is important that their body has a chance to recuperate and not be over stimulated. However, they may still enjoy it if you sing the rhymes to comfort them.

If you or your baby have any health problems or special conditions, seek medical advice before practising the exercises in this book. Please observe all cautions given.

The Sun Has Got His Hat On

Stretch out your arms in front of you, level with your shoulders
so that your baby can see your hands

Stretch out your fingers

The sun has got his hat on
Sway your hands and arms gently from side to side

Hip, hip, hip hooray
Continue swaying your hands

The sun has got his hat on
Continue swaying your hands, and then

And he's coming out to play!
Gently bring your hands on to your baby's chest

Ask your baby **'Do you want to play?'**

On the
CD this
rhyme
is No 1

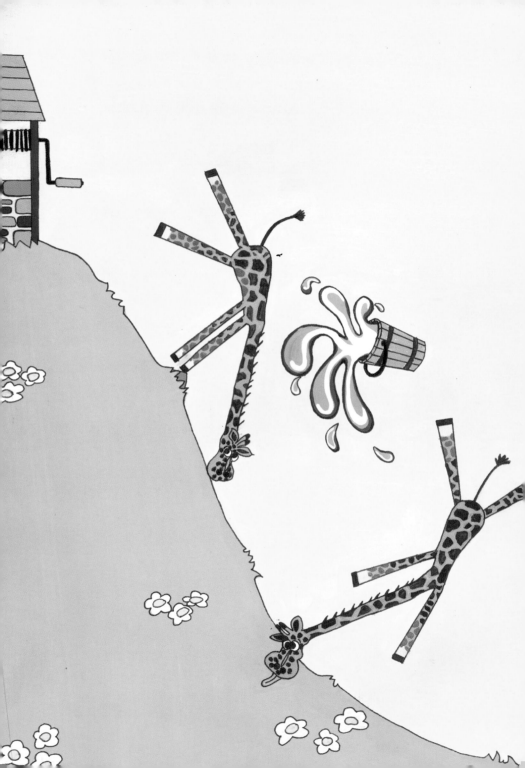

Jack And Jill

Support you baby's legs, by
gently holding their ankles

Carefully bend each knee up towards their chest,
then straighten them again (as if they were marching)

Help your baby 'march' throughout the rhyme

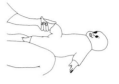

Jack and Jill
Went up the hill
To fetch a pail of water

Jack fell down
And broke his crown
And Jill came tumbling after!

On the
CD this
rhyme
is No 2

The Grand Old Duke Of York

Continue 'marching' throughout the rhyme

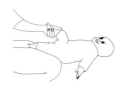

The Grand Old Duke of York
He had ten thousand men
He marched them up to the top
of the hill
And he marched them down again

And when they were up
they were up
And when they were down
they were down
And when they were only half way up
They were neither up nor down!

On the
CD this
rhyme
is No 3

Little Tricycle

Continue 'marching'

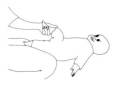

I have a little tricycle
I ride it to the shop
But when I see the big red sign
I know I have to STOP!

As you sing the word 'STOP'
gently straighten and stretch their legs,
and pause for a moment

Start 'marching' again

I have a little tricycle
I ride it to the shop
But when I see the big red sign
I know I have to STOP!

As you sing the word 'STOP',
Gently straighten and stretch their legs,
and stop 'marching'

On the
CD this
rhyme
is No 4

Row, Row, Row Your Boat

Gently hold your baby's ankles and straighten their legs

Throughout all verses, gently but
continually, cross and then uncross your baby's legs.
Each time you cross them, alternate which leg is on top

Row, row, row your boat
Gently down the stream
Merrily, merrily, merrily, merrily
Life is like a dream

Rock, rock, rock your boat
Gently to and fro
Merrily, merrily, merrily, merrily
Into the water we go!
Say 'SPLASH'!

Swim, swim, swim about
Gently down the stream
If you see a crocodile
Don't forget to scream!
Say 'Arhhhh'!

On the
CD this
rhyme
is No 5

Hot Cross Buns

Throughout both verses continue
alternately crossing and uncrossing your baby's legs

Hot cross buns
Hot cross buns
One a penny
Two a penny
Hot cross buns

If you have no daughters
Give them to your sons
One a penny
Two a penny
Hot cross buns

On the
CD this
rhyme
is No 6

Jelly On A Plate

Support one of your baby's legs upright by
holding the thigh between both hands
(As if you were going to make a dough sausage)

Jelly on a plate
Roll their thigh between your hands

Jelly on a plate
Continue rolling

Wibble, wobble
Gently slide your hands over the knee
to their calf, and

Wibble, wobble
Continue rolling

Jelly on a plate
Continue rolling

Change leg and repeat

(It is important to avoid rolling the knee)

On the
CD this
rhyme
is No 7

Pat-A-Cake

Hold your baby's hands

Throughout the rhyme
gently clap their hands together

Pat-a-cake, Pat-a-Cake
Baker's man
Bake me a cake
As fast as you can
Prick it and pat it
And mark it with 'B'
Put it in the oven
For baby and me

On the
CD this
rhyme
is No 8

Windscreen Wipers

Gently hold your baby's wrists, and
Stretch their arms out to the sides

Cross their arms over each other
(as if they were hugging themselves)
Then gently stretch them out to the sides again
Repeat throughout the verse

Windscreen wipers
What do you do all day?
Swish, swosh
Swish, swosh
I wipe the rain away

Crossing your baby's arms across their chest
(as if they were hugging themselves)
Then gently rock your baby from side to side
Repeat throughout the verse

Windscreen wipers
What do you do all day?
Swish, swosh
Swish, swosh
I wipe the rain away

On the
CD this
rhyme
is No 9

I Went To School One Morning

Whilst you are standing up, support your baby by cuddling them close to your chest with one arm and taking their weight with the other hand.
Have their back to your chest, so that they are facing outwards

As you sing the verse, march around the room
I went to school one morning
And I marched like this
I marched like this, I marched like this
I went to school one morning
And I marched like this
All on the way to school

As long as your baby is secure, hold your baby whichever way you are most comfortable

Bend your knees and gently lower your baby towards the floor as you are squatting. Then straighten your legs and lift your baby up towards your chest. Repeat throughout the verse

I went to school one morning
And I jumped like this
I jumped like this, I jumped like this
I went to school one morning
And I jumped like this
All on the way to school

Cuddle your baby to your chest again.
Throughout the verse, slowly turn in circles around the room
(as if you were waltzing)
I went to school one morning
And I waltzed like this
I waltzed like this, I waltzed like this
I went to school one morning
And I waltzed like this
All on the way to school

On the CD this rhyme is No 10

Dance To Your Daddy

Support your baby by laying them along one of your arms,
facing downwards with their head by your elbow

Your arm should support their weight, whilst your
hand is holding the top of a leg firmly

Rest your free hand on their back for extra support.

Throughout the rhyme walk around,
gently swinging them to and fro

Dance to your Daddy
My little babby
Dance to your Daddy
My little lamb

You shall have a fishy
On your little dishy
You shall have a fishy
When the boat comes in

Dance to your Daddy
My little babby
Dance to your Daddy
My little lamb

You shall have a fishy
On your little dishy
You shall have a fishy
When the boat comes in

On the
CD this
rhyme
is No 11

Rock A Bye Baby

Lay on your back
Lift your knees up towards your chest,
keeping your knees together

Lay your baby on the lower part of your legs,
on their front, so that they can look down at you

Make sure you hold them firmly with both of your hands

Throughout the rhyme gently rock your baby,
by tilting the lower part of your legs up and down

Rock a bye baby
On a tree top
When the wind blows
The cradle will rock
When the bough breaks
The cradle will fall
Down will come baby
Cradle and all

On the
CD this
rhyme
is No 12

Ride A Cock Horse To Banbury Cross

Still laying on your back bend your
knees together and put your feet flat on the floor

Sit your baby on your tummy,
with their back against your thighs

Support them with your hands

Slowly push your hips to the ceiling
and then lower them back down again.
Repeat throughout the rhyme
(so that your baby feels like they are horse-riding)

Ride a cock horse
To Banbury Cross
To see a fine lady
On a white horse
Rings on her fingers
And bells on her toes
She shall have music
Wherever she goes

*Young babies will feel
more secure if their head
is supported*

*Older babies may be
happy to sit up during the
exercise*

On the
CD this
rhyme
is No 13

Horsey, Horsey

Continue 'horse riding' throughout the rhyme
Horsey, horsey
Don't you stop
Just let your feet
Go clipperty clop
Your tail goes swish
And the wheels go round
Giddy up
We're homeward bound

*Young babies will feel
more secure if their head
is supported*

*Older babies may be
happy to sit up during the
exercise*

On the
CD this
rhyme
is No 14

Knead The Dough

Sit on the floor with your legs stretched out in front of you
keeping your legs together,
lay your baby across your thighs

Knead the dough
Gently rock your baby to and fro
Knead the dough
Continue rocking
When that side's done
Continue rocking
It's over we go!
Roll them all the way over,
down your legs

Knead the dough
Gently rock your baby to and fro
Knead the dough
Continue rocking
Bake it well
Continue rocking
And watch it grow
Roll them all the way over,
up your legs, back on to your thighs

*(For smaller babies who can not support their own head,
make sure your leg or one hand is supporting their neck)*

On the
CD this
rhyme
is No 15

Me And My Teddy Bear

Use a very thin (preferably slightly see-through) scarf

Throughout the rhyme
gently swish the scarf up and down
from head to toe, above your baby

Me and my teddy bear
Have no worries
Have no care
Me and my teddy bear
We play and play all day

I love my teddy bear
He's got one eye
And he's got no hair
I love my teddy bear
We play and play all day

*(Bigger babies may love this 'Peekaboo' game,
but smaller babies may prefer not to have the scarf over their
face)*

On the
CD this
rhyme
is No 16

Baa Baa Black Sheep

Continue 'swishing' the scarf

Baa baa black sheep
Have you any wool?
Yes Sir, Yes Sir
Three bags full

One for the master
One for the dame
And one for the little boy
Who lives down the lane

On the
CD this
rhyme
is No 17

Two Little Dickie Birds

Place your hands side-by-side
so that your index fingers and thumbs are touching,
Point the index fingers, and tuck your other fingers away,
into your hands

Stretch your arms out in front of you,
so that your baby can see your pointed index fingers

Imagine a figure of eight on its side

Two little dickie birds
Draw the figure of eight in the air
Circling up to your right to begin with

*Finger puppets can be
used for this rhyme*

Sitting on the wall
Continue drawing the figure of eight

One named Peter
Draw with just one finger (to indicate Peter)
Hold the other finger still

One named Paul
Draw with the other finger (to indicate Paul)
hold the 'Peter' finger still

Fly away Peter
Hide 'Peter' finger behind your back

Fly away Paul
Hide 'Paul' finger behind your back

Come back Peter
Bring back 'Peter' finger

Come back Paul
Bring back 'Paul' finger,
Draw a final figure of eight with both fingers
(remembering to circle up to the right first of all)

On the
CD this
rhyme
is No 18

Little Boats

Gently hold your baby's left ankle and the right wrist

Bring their foot and hand together (making the shape
of a sail)
Then, stretch them out again
Repeat to the end of the verse

Little boats are sailing on the water
Up and down, up and down
Little boats are sailing on the water
Up and down, up and down

Change over so that you are holding your baby's other ankle
and wrist
Repeat, as before, throughout the verse

Little ducks are bobbing on the water
Up and down, up and down
Little ducks are bobbing on the water
Up and down, up and down

Gently hold both of your baby's ankles
Slightly parting the legs, carefully bend the knees up towards
their tummy
Bring their knees together and then straighten their legs
(It will look as if they are doing breaststroke with their legs)
Repeat to the end of the verse

Little fish are swimming in the water
Round and round, round and round
Little fish are swimming in the water
Round and round, round and round

Gently hold both of your baby's wrists
Stretch out their arms to the side
Gently stretch them up above their head, then back
down again
Repeat throughout this verse (as if they were flying)

Little seagulls flying o'er the water
In and out, in and out
Little seagulls flying o'er the water
In and out, and all day long

On the
CD this
rhyme
is No 19

Sleep Baby Sleep

Support your baby by laying them along one of your arms, facing
downwards with their head by your elbow

Your arm should support their weight, whilst your
hand is holding the top of a leg firmly

Rest your free hand on their back for extra support

*(Just as you did for 'Dance to your Daddy', but this time
sitting down)*

Very gently rock them to and fro
Sleep baby sleep
Your father tends the sheep
Your Mother shakes the dreamland tree
And from it fall sweet dreams for thee
Sleep baby sleep
Sleep baby sleep

Sleep baby sleep
Our cottage vale is deep
A little lamb is on the green
With snowy fleece so soft and clean
Sleep baby sleep
Sleep baby sleep

On the
CD this
rhyme
is No 20

Useful Contacts

Touch-Needs - stock a wide range of books, nursery rhyme and relaxing CDs and other products
01889 560260
www.touchneeds.com

Touch-Learn - if you wish to find a Rhythm Kids or Infant Massage teacher in your area .
01889 566222
www.touchlearn.co.uk

Guild of Infant and Child Massage - support professionals, parents, infants and children
01889 564555
www.gicm.org.uk

Association for Post-Natal Illness - offers support to mothers suffering from postnatal illness
020 7386 0868
www.apni.org

La Leche League - offers support for breastfeeding mothers and their families
020 7242 1278
www.laleche.org.uk

National Childbirth Trust - supports parents during pregnancy, birth and beyond
0870 444 8707
www.nct-online.org

National NEWPIN - helps families under stress to achieve positive changes in their lives
020 7358 5900
www.newpin.org.uk

National Council for One Parent Families - promotes the welfare of one-parent families
020 7482 4851
www.ncopf.org.uk

Alison Carpenter-Hughes
For all illustrations and paintings
0116 2750054